DROWNED PLANET

Contents

by Sally Odgers
illustrated by Georgina Thomas

SCHOLASTIC

T H E   A R K I E S

Reading Manga: What is it?

The Japanese word 'manga' has been used for nearly 200 years. It means whimsical pictures (man = whimsical, ga = pictures).

Today, manga is a label for Japanese-style graphic novels, comic books and animated movies (also called anime). What's the difference between a graphic novel and a comic book? The answer is in your hands. Graphic novels are usually quality productions, some-times run to hundreds of pages, and often cover serious subjects. Many Japanese manga focus on topics like the environment, the law, science, history – you name it.

Manga don't all look exactly the same, but they have some things in common:

Big Eyes

Oversized Expressions

Fast Action

Reading Manga:
How to Follow

Each page of a graphic novel is divided into boxes called panels. You follow the panels from left to right and top to bottom, like this:

Each panel is like a paragraph in a regular book. It shows you where the characters are, and what they are doing, saying and thinking.

Some panels include a little box at the top (or the bottom), giving you information about what's going on. These are called captions.

SOMEONE IS WATCHING THE ARKIES ...

DID YOU KNOW?

Traditional Japanese manga look a little different. That's because in Japan, people read from right to left. Japanese manga is read like this:

It's easier than it looks!

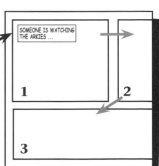

Reading Manga: Who's talking?

Speech balloons tell you who is speaking, what they're saying, and how.

THIS IS A SPEECH BALLOON.

PSST. I'M WHISPERING. CAN YOU TELL?

THIS IS HOW I SHOUT!

NOW I'M THINKING.

Sometimes the lettering changes, to tell you which words are most important. These words might appear in **BOLD** or LARGE TYPE or in *ITALICS*.

Sometimes a punctuation point is enough to explain what's going on.

And how would you show an alien language? Maybe like this:

Reading Manga:
What's that sound?

When you read speech bubbles, you hear manga characters' voices inside your head. There's a way to hear the background noises too – the rumble of thunder, the ringing of a telephone, the crack of a stick underfoot.

Manga artists represent sound effects (or SFX) by placing words over the panels, using lettering to suit each particular sound. It looks like this:

Scary sound

Mechanical sound

Quiet sound

DID YOU KNOW?

Japanese manga SFX are very precise. For example, *bicha bicha* means small splash, *bashan* is a medium splash, and *zaban* is a very big splash. There's even an SFX for total silence: *shiin*.

SFX are used to show emotions as well. The word *unzori* placed next to a character tells you they're feeling bored. If it was *moji moji* they'd be feeling shy, and *shobo shobo* indicates sadness.

Reading Manga:
What's that look on your face?

Manga characters have exaggerated expressions, to help you understand what they're feeling. The first feature everyone notices is the eyes, which may be wide open in:

Shock

Fear

Hope

Closed eyes can mean:

Laughter

Sadness

Noses and chins are more difficult to spot (some characters have no nose at all). This reflects the Japanese preference for delicate features. In manga, big noses and chins are kept for the bad guys.

Reading Manga:

What's that look on your face?

Just like manga characters' eyes, manga mouths are either huge or tiny. A big, wide-open mouth indicates:

Fear

Anger

Happiness

A character with a little mouth may be feeling:

Sad

Thoughtful

Shy

You can also tell a lot about manga characters from the crazy colour or style of their hair. For example, blue hair can mean the character is cool-headed, while orange hair equals determination (and sometimes a fiery temper). Wild, spiky hairstyles show the character is adventurous.

Characters

The Arkies

Singer

Gentle Singer can sense the mind of any living being, and communicate by thought alone. She understands many languages.

Lyam

Science whiz Lyam can tell the Arkies everything they need to know about alien plant and animal life – and then some.

Merlinna

Merlinna is always ready for a battle. She's an expert with weapons – including her naturally piercing screech.

Pace

Pace is a practical guy with a very practical skill – he can communicate with electronic equipment. He and Singer are special friends.

EarthNet

Tench and Farla are EarthNet agents who trail the *Ark3*. They want to capture the Arkies and return them to Earth.

Tench   Farla

INSIDE THE EXPLORATION SHIP, ARK3 ...

OUR NEXT MISSION IS A LITTLE DIFFERENT ...

ARKMA, THEY'RE ALL DIFFERENT.

ARKMA SHOWS THE ARKIES A HOLOGRAM.

THE ARKIES JOB IS TO FIND SETTLEMENT-READY (S-R) PLANETS ...

WE DON'T KNOW MUCH ABOUT MOST PLANETS WE EXPLORE. HOWEVER, THIS ONE IS QUITE WELL-DOCUMENTED.

THEN WHY ARE WE GOING DOWN, ARKMA?

... THE POPULATION GREW. THE CITIES PRODUCED TOO MUCH POLLUTION.

THE PLANET WAS SETTLED LONG AGO. FOR MANY YEARS THE SOCIETY THRIVED BUT ...

THE ARKIES ARE SHOCKED.

DIDN'T PEOPLE LEARN FROM WHAT NEARLY HAPPENED TO EARTH?

THE PEOPLE OF THIS PLANET NEVER HEARD OF EARTH.

DIDN'T THEY COME FROM THERE ORIGINALLY?

EARTH IS NOT THE ONLY PLANET TO DEVELOP INDUSTRIAL CIVILISATION. NOR ARE HUMANS THE ONLY SPECIES TO BRING THEIR PLANET TO THE BRINK OF DISASTER.

THE POPULATION WAS EVACUATED. THEY VANISHED AMONG THE STARS.

THE ARK MASTERS RETRIEVED A CAPSULE SHOWING THE CALAMITY. THEY HAVE CHOSEN YOU TO CHECK THE CURRENT STATUS OF THE PLANET.

THAT IS DIFFERENT. I GUESS WE'RE NOT LOOKING FOR AN S-R PLANET BUT AN R-R ONE.

R-R?

HE MEANS RESETTLEMENT-READY, LYAM.

MERLINNA AND SINGER HAVE SERIOUS QUESTIONS.

WE DON'T KNOW, MERLINNA.

IS THERE ANYTHING ALIVE DOWN THERE?

WHAT ABOUT EARTHNET? ARE THEY LIKELY TO TURN UP?

DON'T THEY ALWAYS? SO, BE ON YOUR GUARD ...

ARK3 DROPS TOWARDS THE DROWNED PLANET.

- 13 -

SUDDENLY —

WHAT HAPPENED?

WHA – OUCH!

WE STOPPED.

SOMETHING HAS BROUGHT ARK3 TO A HALT.

THIS IS OUTSIDE INTERFERENCE!

THIS IS FARLA FETTLEMAN OF THE VESSEL EARTHNET. WE HAVE YOUR SHIP IN OUR LINK-LIKE-LOCK BEAM.

HOW CAN THEY DO THAT? WE'RE IN NEUTRAL SPACE.

ARKMA, CAN YOU GET LOOSE?

THERE IS ONE THING WE MIGHT TRY …

ARKMA EXPLAINS HER PLAN.

THE LINK-LIKE-LOCK BEAM HAS LOCKED ONTO OUR HULL. IF YOU USE THE—

AND THAT'S NOT ALL …

REPEAT. WE ARE HOLDING YOUR SHIP. YOU MUST NOT INTERFERE WITH THIS PLANET.

GOTCHA, ARKMA IF I CONVERT TH HULL MATERIAL TO A DIFFERENT ALLOY THE BEAM WILL SLIP.

chapter 2 : Under the Water

ARK3 COMES TO REST ON A TINY ISLAND.

OK PACE, CONVERT THE WHOLE HULL TO RESEMBLE ROCK. THAT WILL CAMOUFLAGE ARK3 ...

ARKMA GIVES THE ARKIES MOUTHPIECES, TO FILTER OXYGEN FROM THE WATER.

YOU WILL NEED IT. YOU'RE GOING TO SPEND A LOT OF TIME UNDER WATER.

IS EVERYONE CLEAR ON WHAT WE'RE LOOKING FOR?

ANY SIGN OF DANGER. HOW DO WE TALK?

I'LL LINK US IN A CHAIN.

A CHAIN? I HATE CHAINING.

THE ARKIES BEGIN TO EXPLORE.

THE EARTHNET AGENTS HAVE FINALLY REGAINED CONTROL OF THEIR SHIP.

FARLA IS NOT PLEASED.

YOU TOLD ME THAT LINK-LIKE-LOCK BEAM WOULD WORK!

IT SHOULD HAVE. I SET IT TO TITANIUM. THAT'S WHAT THE ARK-SHIPS ARE HULLED WITH.

IT SEEMED TO LOCK ON CORRECTLY ...

UNTIL IT SNAPPED AND TOSSED US HALFWAY ACROSS THE SOLAR SYSTEM! GET US BACK THERE!

THE ARKIES SURVEY YET ANOTHER ISLAND.

WHO'S THE FISHY DUDE THERE?

IT'S JUST A STATUE.

DEEP IN THE OCEAN ...

WHAT? WHAT? HAVE I SLEPT SO LONG?

LOOK AT THE DAMAGE TO THE STONE!

THIS PLANET HAD SERIOUS ACID RAIN, PACE.

THE ARKIES THINK THEY ARE ALONE, BUT —

... SERIOUS ACID RAIN, PACE.

WHO'S THERE? WHAT IS 'PACE'?

UNDER THE WATER, SINGER NEEDS TO COMMUNICATE.

CHAIN TIME, PACE.

I HATE CHAINING.

SINGER HAS SEEN A SHADOW IN THE SEA.

I THINK THERE'S SOMETHING AHEAD.

MORE ROCK?

IT'S THE WRONG OUTLINE FOR THAT. IT'S MANMADE.

OR MONSTER-MADE. LET ME GO FIRST.

THE ARKIES APPROACH WITH CAUTION.

WE'LL FOLLOW YOU, MERLINNA.

THERE'S A PICTURE OF THAT FISHY-DUDE.

THE HATCH IS STUCK FAST.

CLOOOOONK

LITTLE BRO, LET'S RUST THIS!

GOTCHA!

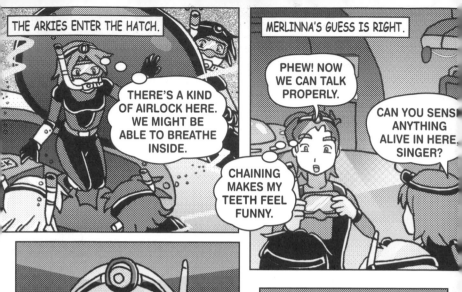

HERE'S THE FISHY-DUDE AGAIN, AND THIS TIME HE'S GOT A HEAD.

A FISH HEAD?

NO, IT LOOKS ALMOST—

HUMAN!

THE ARKIES EXAMINE THE PICTURE.

DOES THIS MEAN THE PEOPLE WHO LIVED HERE WERE MERMAIDS?

OF COURSE NOT. IT LOOKS SORT OF LIKE A SEAL TO ME. UGLY DUDE.

THE ARKIES INSPECT ANOTHER ISLAND.

THERE'S NOTHING LIVING DOWN THERE ... BUT ...

THE WATER SEEMS PURE.

BUT?

I SENSE SOMETHING HERE. SOMETHING HOSTILE ... IT SEEMS ALMOST HUMAN.

LET'S GO!

IF THE WATER AND AIR HAVE CLEARED ... AND IF THE CLIMATE HAS STABILISED ...

THIS MEANS THE PLANET MIGHT BE S-R! GREAT, EH GUYS?

GUYS?

chapter 3 : Tryphon

LYAM IS CAPTURED!

GOTCHA!

GET OFF ME!

NOT A CHANCE. WE'VE LOST YOU TOO OFTEN. NOW YOU'RE COMING ABOARD OUR SHIP.

THE YO-CHUTE WON'T TAKE THREE.

TAKE HIM UP WITH YOU, THEN COME BACK FOR ME.

C'MON, KID. THIS HURTS ME MORE THAN IT DOES YOU.

IF YOU THINK THAT, YOU'RE AN IDIOT.

THEIR CAPTOR SURVEYS THE ARKIES.

AIR BREATHERS?

YOU'RE – KILLING – US –

YES – YES –

LET US GO!!!

THE MONSTER GLIDES TOWARDS A CAVERN IN THE UNDERWATER CLIFF ...

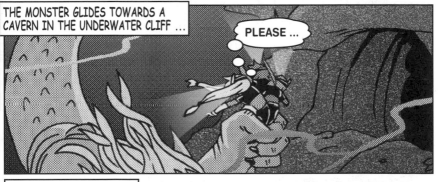

PLEASE ...

... ENTERS A CAVERN, AND SETS THE ARKIES DOWN.

MAN, AM I GLAD TO BE ABLE TO TALK AGAIN!

IT – IT'S HUGE!

GREETINGS, MINIONS. BOW TO ME.

BUT – WHY DO YOU SPEAK OUR LANGUAGE?

AND WHY HAVE YOU KIDNAPPED US? WHERE'S LYAM?

IT IS A GOD'S BUSINESS TO SPEAK THE LANGUAGE OF ALL PEOPLE. NOW, BOW – OR DIE.

THE ARKIES ARE AMAZED, BUT THEY BOW AS DIRECTED.

YOU'RE A GOD? BUT—

I AM TRYPHON, LORD OF THE DEEPS, MASTER OF THE TIDES AND KEEPER OF TIME WHY HAVE YOU COME TO ME?

WE DIDN'T COME TO YOU. YOU GRABBED US.

SIR – UM – TRYPHON? WE ARE ARKIES. WE CAME TO EXPLORE ... UM ...

THE ARKIES EXPLAIN THEIR MISSION TO TRYPHON.

SO YOU SEE, WE ARE JUST VISITING.

WHERE IS LYAM?

YOUR FRIEND IS NO LONGER ON MY LAND OR IN MY SEA.

BUT HE WAS RIGHT BEHIND US ...

YOUR LAND? DO YOU KNOW WHAT HAPPENED TO IT?

MY PEOPLE SOURED THE SEA AND FOULED THE LAND! THEY LET MY STATUES ROT WHERE THEY STOOD! I SENT THEM RAIN AND WIND TO CLEANSE THE LAND AND WHAT DID THEY DO?

THEY ABANDONED ME!

BUT TRYPHON, IT WAS POLLUTION THAT CAUSED THE CLIMATE CHANGE AND FLOODED THE PLANET.

HAVE I NOT JUST SAID SO??? AND NOW I MUST BE GONE.

AFTER TRYPHON LEAVES, THE ARKIES DISCUSS THEIR SITUATION.

IS THIS DUDE FOR REAL?

I DON'T THINK HE IS A GOD ... EXACTLY.

WHO CARES WHAT HE IS? WE'VE GOT TO FIND LYAM!

TRYPHON SAYS HE'S NOT HERE.

YOU BELIEVE THAT THING KNOWS?

IF WE CAN MAKE FRIENDS WITH TRYPHON HE MIGHT HELP US FIND LYAM.

YOU DON'T MAKE FRIENDS WITH MONSTERS AND KIDNAPPERS. YOU FIGHT THEM!

MEANWHILE, IN THE EARTHNET VESSEL, HIGH ABOVE THE PLANET ...

GET IN THERE AND STAY THERE!

UGHHHH!

FARLA FETTLEMAN IS WAITING FOR TENCH TO RETURN.

ONE ARKIE IN THE NET. THREE MORE TO GO. BUT WHAT'S TAKING TENCH SO LONG? I SHOULD HAVE GONE MYSELF.

HOW TO GET THE OTHERS? MAYBE WE COULD USE HIM AS BAIT. HMMMM.

chapter 4 : A Fair Trade

GOOD. HE'S GONE. NOW ... A BIT OF OIL FOR THESE BOLTS.

TENCH RETURNS TO WHERE HE LEFT FARLA.

I CAGED THE KID, FARLA. FARLA?

USING HIS SCIENTIFIC SAMPLES, LYAM HAS MANAGED TO UNDO THE BOLTS OF HIS CAGE.

NOW ... HOW DO I GET OUT OF THIS ONE?

TRYPHON WATCHES THE ARKIES AND FARLA.

WHERE'S LYAM?

HE'S SAFE IN EARTHNET'S CARE. IT'S YOUR FAULT.

I SEE YOU ARE AS QUARRELSOME AS MY PEOPLE WERE.

YOU WILL LEARN BETTER, ONE DAY.

BUT YOU CAN'T KEEP US HERE, TRYPHON!

WELL ... YOU COULD KEEP FARLA. IF YOU TREAT HER KINDLY.

TRYPHON IS FURIOUS.

I SENSE YOU ARE A GOOD – UM – GOD. GOOD GODS DON'T NEED TO BULLY PEOPLE. WHAT USE ARE COMPANIONS IF YOU FORCE THEM TO STAY WITH YOU?

STOP TALKING RUBBISH! I DEMAND THAT YOU LET ME TAKE THESE CHILDREN!

I AM A GOD! YOU CANNOT TELL ME WHAT I MUST DO!

TRYPHON LEAVES THE CAVERN ...

WHAT ARE WE GOING TO DO? WE MIGHT BE ABLE TO SWIM OUT ... BUT HE'D CATCH US.

FARLA CAN'T. SHE HASN'T GOT BREATHING GEAR.

I JUST HAD AN IDEA ... BUT WE NEED ARKMA'S HELP.

IT ALL DEPENDS ON WHETHER THIS BRAIN IS BROKEN ...

MEANWHILE ...

CAUTION! CAUTION! ENTERING LOWER ATMOSPHERE! MAY NOT BE ABLE TO TAKE OFF AGAIN ...

I'M GONNA LAND THIS BABY!

GOOD.

LYAM ARRIVES BACK ON THE PLANET IN STYLE.

GERONIMOOOOO!

MEANWHILE ...

B–B–B–UTTTT ... W–W– WHATTT?

MY NEW PEOPLE WANT THEIR FRIEND. WHAT HAVE YOU DONE WITH HIM?

BACK IN THE CAVERN ...

YOU SURE YOU WANT TO STAY BEHIND?

YES. WE HAVE TO EXPLAIN TO TRYPHON.

PACE ARRIVES BACK AT ARK3 TO FIND LYAM THERE ALREADY.

LYAM! HOW DID YOU GET HERE?

IT'S A LONG STORY. WHERE DID YOU GO?

AND WHERE ARE THE OTHERS?

MUST GET TO ARKMA ... MUST HURRY!

- 37 -

LATER ...

THIS IS YOUR FAULT, TENCH.

WHAT IS YOUR REPORT, ARKIES?

THE PLANET HAS RECOVERED WELL, BUT THERE ISN'T MUCH SOLID GROUND.

BESIDES ... TRYPHON MIGHT GET IDEAS AGAIN.

SO, PACE, WHAT IS YOUR CONCLUSION?

NOT S-R. WHAT A WASTE OF TIME.

I THINK WE CAN CALL IT A SUCCESSFUL MISSION.

DROWNED PLANET
Official Arkie report.
NOT S-R.

Drowned Planet Cosmopedia

Arkies Teenagers who seek out new Settlement-Ready planets.

Ark3 The Arkies' spacecraft.

ArkMa The electronic mind that flies *Ark3*. A shipbrain.

Chaining Mind-talking through linked hands.

Didgies Indigenous inhabitants of a planet.

EarthNet An organisation that wants to send the Arkies home.

Link-Like-Lock beam A magnetic beam that locks like material together: iron to iron, stone to stone etc.

MatCon A matter converter, used to convert matter into useful objects.

S-R (Settlement-Ready) Planets with oxygen, water, vegetation, metal and no intelligent didgies.

Shipbrain The electronic mind of an Arkie ship.

Tangle-line A weapon that tangles around arms or legs, and stings but does not injure.

Yo-chute An electronic line EarthNet agents use to travel up and down from their orbiting ships.